SOAR TO SUCC

THE READING INTERVENTION PROGRAM

M000086773

Student Guide

Level 5

Senior Author
J. David Cooper

Authors
Irene Boschken
Janet McWilliams
Lynne Pistochini

HOUGHTON MIFFLIN   BOSTON • MORRIS PLAINS, NJ

California • Colorado • Georgia • Illinois • New Jersey • Texas

Design, Production and Illustration: PiperStudiosInc

2001 Impression.

Printed in the U.S.A.

ISBN: 0-395-78133-7

18 19 20 21 22 23 24 25-WC-05 04 03 02 01

SOAR TO SUCCESS

Contents

SOAR TO SUCCESS

Name _____

REFLECTION

1

What did Nicholas think after his mother told him he couldn't have any mice?

_____

_____

_____

_____

_____

_____

REFLECTION

2

Why did Nicholas take the owlet down from the tree?

_____

_____

_____

_____

_____

_____

Name _____

3

Circle the strategy you used the most so far.

Strategy Box			
Predict	**Summarize**	**Clarify**	**Question**

Name at least one place where you used this strategy. Write the page number(s).

_____

_____

_____

How did this strategy help you?

_____

_____

_____

_____

_____

Name _____

REFLECTION

4

Do you think Owlbert should stay with Nicholas's family?

_____

Why or why not?

_____

_____

_____

_____

_____

Name _____

REFLECTION

Why do you think the emperor penguins huddle together?

_____

_____

_____

REFLECTION

2

Summarize how the emperor penguin parents take turns taking care of their eggs and chicks.

_____

_____

_____

_____

_____

Name _____

REFLECTION

Circle the strategy you used the most so far.

Strategy Box			
Predict	Summarize	Clarify	Question

Name at least one place where you used this strategy. Write the page number(s).

_____

_____

_____

How did this strategy help you?

_____

_____

_____

_____

_____

Name _____

REFLECTION

4

How can we make sure that people share Antarctica fairly with the animals and birds?

_____

_____

_____

_____

_____

_____

_____

Name _____

REFLECTION

1

How do you think Truman felt about all the aunts? Why did he feel that way?

_____

_____

_____

REFLECTION

2

Summarize what Truman did to take care of his aunts.

_____

_____

_____

_____

_____

Truman's Aunt Farm

Name _____

3

Circle the section you liked best in *Truman's Aunt Farm.*

Pages 3–8
Aunts arrive instead
of ants.

Pages 9–19
Truman feeds and
trains the aunts.

Pages 20–27
Truman gives the
aunts away.

How did one or more of the four strategies help you read that
section?

Predict _____

_____

Clarify _____

_____

Summarize _____

_____

Question _____

_____

Name _____

REFLECTION

4

Do you agree with Aunt Fran that Truman "did a wonderful thing"?

_____

Explain.

_____

_____

_____

_____

_____

My Notes to Clarify

Write any words or ideas that you need to clarify. Include the page number.

Words or Ideas	Page
Pages 4–7	
Pages 8–13	
Pages 14–17	
Pages 18–22	

Name _____

REFLECTION

1

What do you think throwing away a lot of trash might do to the environment? Why?

_____

_____

_____

_____

_____

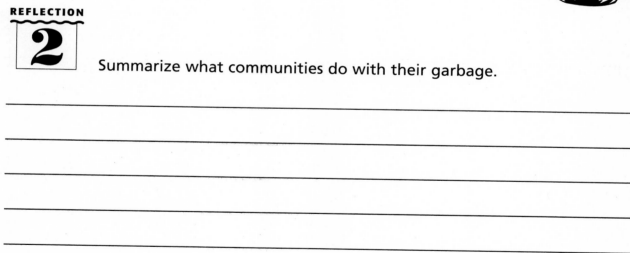

REFLECTION

2

Summarize what communities do with their garbage.

_____

_____

_____

_____

_____

Name _____

REFLECTION 3 Circle the section you liked best so far in *Where Does Garbage Go?* How did one or more of the four strategies help you read that section?

Pages 4–7
The environment and garbage

Pages 8–13
How we get rid of garbage

Pages 14–17
Toxic dangers

Predict _____

_____

Summarize _____

_____

Clarify _____

_____

Question _____

_____

REFLECTION 4

What do you think people should do to produce less garbage?

_____

_____

Name _____

My Notes to Clarify

Write any words or ideas that you need to clarify. Include the page numbers.

Words or Ideas	Page
Pages 2–9	
Pages 10–15	
Pages 16–22	
Pages 23–27	
Pages 28–32	

Name _____

REFLECTION

1

What caused the *Atocha* to sink?

_____

_____

_____

REFLECTION

2

Summarize what the crew did to search for the *Atocha.*

_____

_____

_____

_____

_____

Name _____

REFLECTION

3 Circle the section you liked best so far in *Sunken Treasure.* How did one or more of the four strategies help you read that section?

Pages 2–9
The sinking and Spanish search

Pages 10–15
Mel Fisher's search

Pages 16–22
The find and salvage

Predict

_____

_____

Summarize

_____

_____

Clarify

_____

_____

Question

_____

_____

Sunken Treasure

Name _____

REFLECTION 4

Which would you rather do, bring up treasure or help to preserve it?

_____

Why?

_____

_____

_____

REFLECTION 5

Circle the sunken ship that interests you the most. Then write why it interests you.

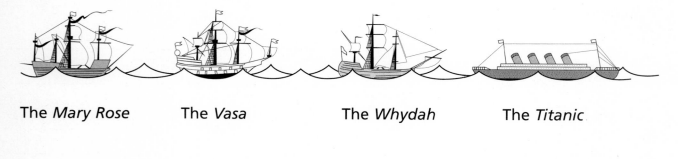

The *Mary Rose*   The *Vasa*   The *Whydah*   The *Titanic*

_____

_____

_____

Name _____

My Notes to Clarify

Write any words or ideas that you need to clarify. Include the page number.

Words or Ideas	Page
Pages 4–11	
Pages 12–19	
Pages 20–29	

Name _____

REFLECTION

1

Summarize how Fernando made his paints.

_____

_____

_____

_____

REFLECTION

2

Do you think Fernando's idea for solving his problem
was a good one?

_____

Explain your answer.

_____

_____

_____

Name _____

REFLECTION

3   Think about how you used strategies with *The Little Painter of Sabana Grande.*

Write how you used one or more of the four strategies below.

Predict

_____

_____

_____

Question

_____

_____

_____

Clarify

_____

_____

_____

Summarize

_____

_____

_____

Name _____

Story Map

Title

Setting

Characters

Problem

Major Events

Outcome

Name _____

My Notes to Clarify

Write any words or ideas that you need to clarify. Include the page numbers.

Words or Ideas	Page
Pages 4–11	
Pages 12–19	
Pages 20–27	
Pages 28–32	

Name _____

1

How would you describe Taro?

_____

_____

_____

2

How did the merchant feel about his daughter marrying Taro?

_____

_____

Why did he feel that way?

_____

_____

_____

Name _____

REFLECTION

3

Summarize what the merchant had to do before Taro's mother gave her consent.

_____
_____
_____
_____

REFLECTION

4

Circle the strategy you used most.

Strategy Box			
Predict	Summarize	Clarify	Question

Name at least one place where you used this strategy. Write the page number(s).

_____
_____

How did this strategy help you?

_____
_____

Name _____

K-W-L Chart

Title

What I **K**now	What I **W**ant to Find Out	What I **L**earned

Name _____

My Notes to Clarify

Write any words or ideas that you need to clarify. Include the page
numbers.

Words or Ideas	Page
Pages 4–9	
Pages 10–13	
Pages 14–19	
Pages 20–23	
Pages 24–32	

Name _____

REFLECTION

1

Why do you think some birds have two different homes, one in the north, and one in the south?

_____

_____

_____

_____

REFLECTION

2

How do bird bands show how far a bird has traveled?

_____

_____

_____

_____

Name _____

REFLECTION

3

Summarize some different ways birds find their way south.

_____

_____

_____

_____

REFLECTION

4

Do you think it was a good idea to experiment with the homing pigeon?

_____

Why or why not?

_____

_____

_____

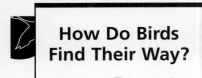

Name _____

REFLECTION

Circle the section you liked best so far in *How Do Birds Find Their Way?*

Pages 4–9	**Pages 10–13**	**Pages 14–19**	**Pages 20–23**	**Pages 24–32**
Describing migration	Where birds go	How birds find their way, Part I	How birds find their way, Part II	Knowing when to fly; How high?

How did one or more of the four strategies help you read that section?

Predict

_____

_____

_____

Summarize

_____

_____

_____

Clarify

_____

_____

_____

Question

_____

_____

Name _____

Story Map

Title
_____

Setting
_____

Characters
_____

Problem
_____

Major Events
_____

Outcome
_____

Name _____

My Notes to Clarify

Write any words or ideas that you need to clarify. Include the page numbers.

Words or Ideas	Page
Pages 4–7	
Pages 8–11	
Pages 12–19	
Pages 20–25	
Pages 26–32	

Name _____

REFLECTION

Do you think Carlos and his sisters will like going to Mexico? Why or why not?

_____

_____

_____

REFLECTION

2

Why do you think Dolores said that she didn't see Mama and Papa getting many opportunities?

_____

_____

_____

Name _____

REFLECTION

3

Circle the strategy you used most in *Going Home*.

Strategy Box			
Predict	Summarize	Clarify	Question

Name at least one place where you used this strategy. Write the page number(s).

_____

_____

How did this strategy help you read that section?

_____

_____

_____

_____

Name _____

REFLECTION

4

Do you agree that Mama and Papa were wise to leave La Perla? Why or why not?

_____

_____

_____

REFLECTION

5

How did Carlos feel about his parents and La Perla? Why did he feel that way?

_____

_____

_____

_____

Mountain Gorillas in Danger

Name _____

K-W-L Chart

Title		

What I **K**now	What I **W**ant to Find Out	What I **L**earned
_____	_____	_____
_____	_____	_____
_____	_____	_____
_____	_____	_____
_____	_____	_____
_____	_____	_____
_____	_____	_____
_____	_____	_____
_____	_____	_____
_____	_____	_____
_____	_____	_____
_____	_____	_____
_____	_____	_____
_____	_____	_____
_____	_____	_____

Name _____

My Notes to Clarify

Write any words or ideas that you need to clarify. Include the page numbers.

Words or Ideas	Page
Pages 4–7	
Pages 8–11	
Pages 12–17	
Pages 18–23	
Pages 24–29	

Mountain Gorillas in Danger

Name _____

Think about the features of a mountain gorilla. How have they helped the gorilla adapt to living in the mountains?

_____

_____

_____

It takes many years for mountain gorillas to start new families. Why is that dangerous for the 400 gorillas left?

_____

_____

_____

Name _____

REFLECTION

3 Summarize the dangers mountain gorillas may face from farmers.

_____

_____

_____

_____

REFLECTION

4 How do you think gorillas can be helped if people learn more about them?

_____

_____

_____

Mountain Gorillas in Danger

Name _____

REFLECTION

5

Circle the section you liked best in *Mountain Gorillas in Danger.*

Pages 4–7	**Pages 8–11**	**Pages 12–17**	**Pages 18–23**	**Pages 24–32**
Where mountain gorillas live	Gorilla families	Danger from people and new leaders	How people can help	Jobs and studying

How did one or more of the four strategies help you read that section?

Predict _____

_____

Summarize _____

_____

Clarify _____

_____

Question _____

_____

Name _____

Story Map

Title
[ ]

Setting
[ ]

Characters
[ ]

Problem
[ ]

Major Events
[ ]

Outcome
[ ]

Name _____

My Notes to Clarify

Write any words or ideas that you need to clarify. Include the page numbers.

Words or Ideas	Page
Pages 4–11 _____	_____
_____	_____
_____	_____
_____	_____
Pages 12–17 _____	_____
_____	_____
_____	_____
_____	_____
_____	_____
Pages 18–25 _____	_____
_____	_____
_____	_____
_____	_____
Pages 26–31 _____	_____
_____	_____
_____	_____
_____	_____

Name _____

REFLECTION

1   How would you describe Spider?

_____

_____

_____

REFLECTION

2   Do you think Spider's father and grandmother gave him
good advice? Explain.

_____

_____

_____

_____

_____

_____

REFLECTION

3 Summarize how Spider decided he would go to the spelling bee.

_____

_____

_____

REFLECTION

4   Circle the section you liked best in *Brave as a Mountain Lion*.

Pages 12–17
Brave as a mountain
lion, clever as
a coyote

Pages 18–25
Silent as a spider

Pages 26–31
The spelling
bee

How did one or more of the four strategies help you read that section?

Predict _____

_____

Clarify _____

_____

Summarize _____

_____

Question _____

_____

Name _____

Event Map

Title

Event 1

Event 2

Event 3

Event 4

Event 5

Event 6

Event 7

Event 8

Name _____

My Notes to Clarify

Write any words or ideas that you need to clarify. Include the page numbers.

Words or Ideas	Page
Pages 4–9 _____	_____
_____	_____
_____	_____
_____	_____
Pages 10–15 _____	_____
_____	_____
_____	_____
Pages 16–21 _____	_____
_____	_____
_____	_____
Pages 22–29 _____	_____
_____	_____
_____	_____
_____	_____

Name _____

REFLECTION

1

Why did park rangers let the fires burn at first?

_____

_____

_____

REFLECTION

2

Do you think the rangers should have stopped the fire sooner?

_____

Why or why not?

_____

_____

_____

Fire! in Yellowstone

Name _____

3 Circle the strategy you found most helpful while reading *Fire! in Yellowstone.*

Strategy Box			
Predict	Summarize	Clarify	Question

How did this strategy help?

_____

_____

_____

_____

_____

Copyright © Houghton Mifflin Company. All rights reserved.

Name _____

REFLECTION

4

Summarize how a forest recovers from a fire.

_____

_____

_____

_____

_____

Name _____

Story Map

Title

Setting

Characters

Problem

Major Events

Outcome

Name _____

My Notes to Clarify

Write any words or ideas that you need to clarify. Include the page numbers.

Words or Ideas	Page
Pages 1–9	
Pages 10–14	
Pages 15–25	
Pages 26–35	
Pages 36–39	

Name _____

REFLECTION

1

Why do you think Marshall wanted a job?

_____

_____

_____

_____

REFLECTION

2

Summarize how Marshall got a job at the bicycle store.

_____

_____

_____

_____

_____

_____

Name _____

REFLECTION

3

Circle the strategy you have used the most so far.

Strategy Box			
Predict	Summarize	Clarify	Question

Name at least one place where you used this strategy. Write the page numbers.

_____

_____

How did this strategy help you?

_____

_____

_____

_____

Name _____

REFLECTION

4

What happened to George Pepper in the ten-mile race?

_____

_____

_____

REFLECTION

5

How did Marshall's family react to his medal?

_____

_____

CHAMPION
OF INDIANAPOLIS

_____

_____

_____

Name _____

Main Ideas and Details

Title _____

1. Main idea _____
  a. Detail _____
  b. _____
  c. _____
  d. _____

2. _____
  a. _____
  b. _____
  c. _____
  d. _____

3. _____
  a. _____
  b. _____
  c. _____
  d. _____

4. _____
  a. _____
  b. _____
  c. _____
  d. _____

Name _____

My Notes to Clarify

Write any words or ideas that you need to clarify. Include the page
numbers.

Words or Ideas	Page
Pages 4–7 _____	_____
_____	_____
_____	_____
_____	_____
Pages 8–11 _____	_____
_____	_____
_____	_____
_____	_____
Pages 12–19 _____	_____
_____	_____
_____	_____
_____	_____
Pages 20–24 _____	_____
_____	_____
_____	_____
_____	_____
_____	_____

Name _____

REFLECTION

How do fish eat their prey without using hands?

_____

_____

_____

REFLECTION

Summarize how predator fish hide to catch their prey.

_____

_____

_____

_____

Name _____

REFLECTION

3

Why do people kill sharks?

_____

_____

_____

_____

_____

Name _____

REFLECTION

4

Circle a strategy that helped you.

Strategy Box			
Predict	Summarize	Clarify	Question

Name at least one place where you used this strategy. Write the page number(s).

_____

_____

How did this strategy help you?

_____

_____

_____

_____

_____

Name _____

Event Map

Title	

Event 1	

Event 2	

Event 3	

Event 4	

Event 5	

Event 6	

Event 7	

Event 8	

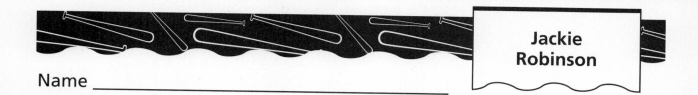

Name _____

My Notes to Clarify

Write any words or ideas that you need to clarify. Include the page numbers.

Words or Ideas	Page
Pages 1–9	
Pages 10–16	
Pages 17–21	
Pages 22–28	
Pages 29–35	
Pages 36–46	
Pages 47–53	

Name _____

REFLECTION

1 Why could Jackie's family go swimming only one day a week?

_____

_____

_____

REFLECTION

2 Why did Jackie Robinson stand out as an unusual athlete?

_____

_____

_____

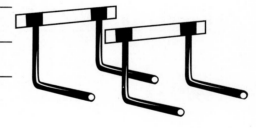

Name _____

REFLECTION

3

Why wasn't Jackie content with winning awards?

_____

_____

_____

REFLECTION

4

Why was Jackie put on trial? What was the result?

_____

_____

_____

_____

Jackie Robinson

Name _____

REFLECTION

5

Summarize how Jackie got to play for a major-league
baseball team.

_____

_____

_____

_____

_____

REFLECTION

6

What hardships did Jackie face when he first
played with the Dodgers?

_____

_____

_____

_____

_____

Name _____

REFLECTION

7

Circle the section of *Jackie Robinson* you liked best.

Pages 1–21	Pages 22–35	Pages 36–53
Jackie, the college athlete	Jackie in the army and signing with the Dodgers	Jackie in the Major Leagues and after

How did one or more of the four strategies help you read that section?

Predict

_____

_____

Clarify

_____

_____

Summarize

_____

_____

Question

_____

_____

Gerbilitis

Name _____

Story Map

Title

Setting

Characters

Problem

Major Events

Outcome

Name _____

My Notes to Clarify

Write any words or ideas that you need to clarify. Include the page numbers.

Words or Ideas	Page
Pages 1–9	
Pages 10–22	
Pages 23–35	
Pages 36–42	
Pages 43–53	
Pages 54–62	
Pages 63–76	

Name _____

REFLECTION
1

Why do you think Garth decided to take care of Weebie?

_____

_____

_____

_____

REFLECTION
2

Do you think Garth's new ability will make him a better pet owner?

_____

Explain.

_____

_____

_____

Name _____

REFLECTION

3

How has Weebie changed the way Garth thinks about animals?

_____

_____

_____

_____

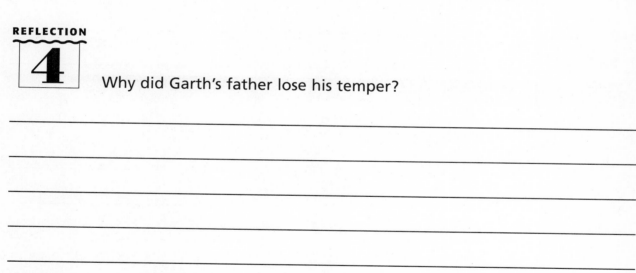

REFLECTION

4

Why did Garth's father lose his temper?

_____

_____

_____

_____

_____

Gerbilitis

Name _____

Circle the strategy you used the most so far.

Strategy Box			
Predict	Summarize	Clarify	Question

Name at least one place where you used this strategy.
Write the page number(s).

_____

_____

How did this strategy help you?

_____

_____

_____

_____

_____

Name _____

REFLECTION

6

What was Weebie's advice to Garth about his parents?

_____
_____
_____
_____

REFLECTION

7

Summarize how the bear helped Garth's parents become closer.

_____
_____
_____
_____
_____

Name _____

K-W-L Chart

Title

What I **K**now	What I **W**ant to Find Out	What I **L**earned

Name _____

My Notes to Clarify

Write any words or ideas that you need to clarify. Include the page numbers.

Words or Ideas	Page
Pages 4–14	
Pages 15–23	
Pages 24–33	
Pages 34–40	

Whales

Name _____

REFLECTION

1

What are two ways in which a whale is different from a fish?

_____

_____

_____

_____

REFLECTION

2

Summarize what you have read about orcas, or killer whales.

_____

_____

_____

_____

_____

Name _____

Whales

REFLECTION

3

Circle the section you liked best so far in *Whales.*

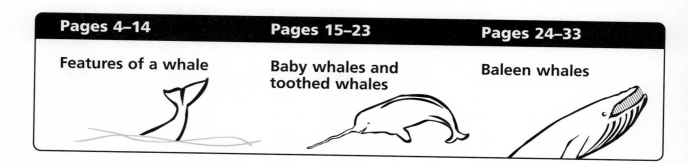

Pages 4–14	Pages 15–23	Pages 24–33
Features of a whale	Baby whales and toothed whales	Baleen whales

How did one or more of the four strategies help you read that section?

Predict

_____

_____

Summarize

_____

_____

Clarify

_____

_____

Question

_____

_____

Whales

Name _____

REFLECTION
4

Why should people care about whales?

_____

_____

_____

_____

_____

Name _____

Story Map

Title

Setting

Characters

Problem

Major Events

Outcome

Name _____

My Notes to Clarify

Write any words or ideas that you need to clarify. Include the page
numbers.

Words or Ideas	Page
Pages 1–12 _____	_____
_____	_____
Pages 13–28 _____	_____
_____	_____
_____	_____
Pages 29–39 _____	_____
_____	_____
_____	_____
Pages 40–46 _____	_____
_____	_____
Pages 47–55 _____	_____
_____	_____
Pages 56–67 _____	_____
_____	_____
_____	_____
Pages 68–83 _____	_____
_____	_____

Name _____

REFLECTION

1

How do you think the panda might be connected to Lu Yi's family being asked to move?

_____

_____

_____

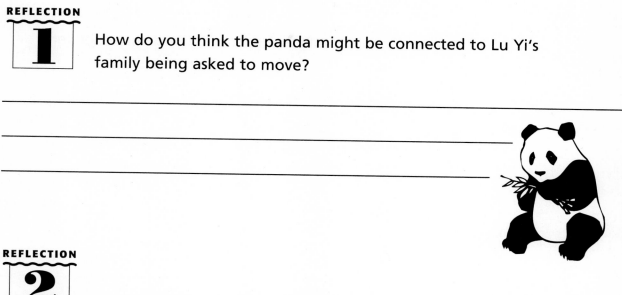

REFLECTION

2

Summarize how Lu Yi took care of the baby panda.

_____

_____

_____

_____

_____

Name _____

REFLECTION

3

Do you think the people should move from their farms so the land can become wild again?

_____

Why or why not?

_____

_____

REFLECTION

4

Why wasn't Lu Yi able to tell the messenger about his baby panda?

_____

_____

_____

Name _____

REFLECTION

5 Circle the section you liked best so far in *The Year of the Panda.*
How did one or more of the four strategies help you read that
section?

Pages 1–12
Mr. Po's panda

Pages 13–28
Finding and
raising Su Lin

Pages 29–46
The messenger

Pages 47–55
The trip to the
Rescue Center

Predict

_____

_____

Summarize

_____

_____

Clarify

_____

_____

Question

_____

_____

The Year of the Panda

Name _____

REFLECTION

6

Do you think the Rescue Center was a good solution to the panda problem?

_____

Explain.

_____

_____

_____

_____

REFLECTION

7

Explain why Lu Yi would make a good animal-research scientist.

_____

_____

_____

_____

Clarify/Phonics How to Say a Word

When I come to a word I don't know, first I look for chunks I know.

I know _____. If I still don't know the word, I look for letter

sounds. In this word, I know the sounds ____, ____, and ____. If I

blend the sounds together, the word is _____.

Finally, I check the meaning by rereading the sentence.

Clarify A Word Meaning

I read this word: _____. I'm not sure what this word

is or what it means. I look at the picture or read to the end of the

sentence. Now I think the word means . . .

Clarify An Idea

I don't understand this idea: _____.

First I _____ (reread, look at pictures, etc.). Then

I understand that . . . I reread the sentence and it makes sense.

Predict

When I predict, I use clues from the pictures or from what I have read to help me figure out what will happen next (or what I will learn). I predict . . .

Question

When I question, I ask something that can be answered as I read or after I finish reading. I might ask . . .

Summarize

When I summarize, I tell in my own words the important things I have read.

Name _____

Book Log

Title	Author	Date Completed	Comments

Name _____

Book Log

Title	Author	Date Completed	Comments